Introduction

The artworks presented here are taken from the archive of *Curtis's Botanical Magazine*, the longest running periodical featuring colour illustrations of plants in the world. Founded in 1787 by apothecary and botanist William Curtis (1746–99), as *The Botanical Magazine*, it appealed to natural history scholars as well as ladies and gentlemen wanting information on the many newly introduced ornamental flowers that were in vogue in the gardens of the wealthy and fashionable. The 19th century saw a proliferation of plant collecting, with new species being sought out to satisfy the Victorian craze for the new and exotic.

Each issue of the magazine contained three hand-coloured, copper-engraved plates alongside the text, which described the Latin name, genus and qualities, along with the plants' botanical, horticultural and historical background, as well as associated information relating to what we might now call conservation, and any economic applications or uses.

Curtis charged one shilling per month and soon had 2,000 subscribers. Accomplished artists were commissioned to produce the plates, and the magazine was an instant success. The plates continued to be hand-coloured until 1948, when a scarcity of colourists led to the implementation of photographic reproduction.

The name of the magazine was changed to *Curtis's Botanical Magazine* after Curtis's death in 1799. It was first produced at Kew in 1841, when William Jackson Hooker (1785–1865) moved south from Glasgow University to become Director of the Royal Botanic Gardens. Joseph Dalton Hooker (1817–1911) took over the role of editor from his father in 1865, and the magazine has continued to be produced by Kew staff and artists to this day.

The artworks included here are by Walter Hood Fitch (1817–92), who illustrated more than 2,700 plants for the magazine and published over 10,000 illustrations in total during his career and also by Matilda Smith (1854–1926), Kew's first official botanical artist, appointed in 1898. She contributed more than 2,300 plates to the magazine over a 40-year period, until 1923.

The plants illustrated come from all over the world, collected by a vast array of plant collectors. Very many of the most popular ornamental plants we grow in our gardens today originate from China, the Far East and South Africa.

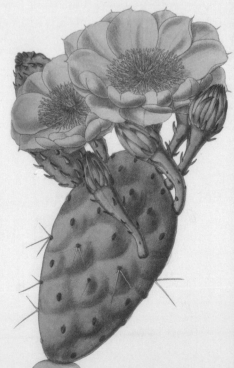

Presented in this compilation are 44 colour plates of plants together with their corresponding black and white lithographs for you to try your hand at colouring. The original watercolour drawings were made from life so you can be sure that your finished renderings will be based on accurate and precise representations of the actual plants. A key to the plates, using plant names given at the time of publication, along with their places of origin may be found in the next few pages.

Key: List of plates

1 *Lycoris squamigera*
Japan

2 *Forsythia suspensa*
Asia

3 *Tricyrtis stolonifera*
East Asia

4 *Lonicera giraldii*
Asia

5 *Rehmannia angulata*
China

6 *Aerides crispum*
India

7 *Podocarpus neriifolia*
Asia, India & the Pacific

8 *Monocera grandiflora*
Asia & India

9 *Epigynium acuminatum*
India & Bhutan

10 *Nymphaea stellata*
Southern & East Asia

11 *Crocus aerius*
Asia

12 *Paeonia peregrina*
Southeastern Europe
& Turkey

13 *Helianthemum ocymoides*
Portugal & Spain

14 *Lithospermum gastonii*
France

15 *Prunus cerasifera*
Europe & Asia

16 *Campanula fragilis*
Italy

17 *Fritillaria aurea*
Turkey

18 *Grammanthes chloraeflora*
South Africa

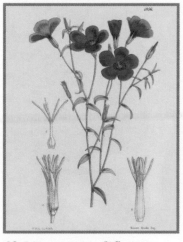

19 *Linum grandiflorum*
Algeria

20 *Spathodea campanulata*
Africa

21 *Tinnea aethiopica*
Africa

22 *Kniphofia rooperi*
South Africa

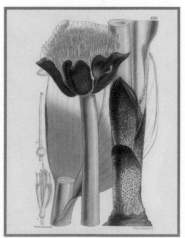

23 *Haemanthus natalensis*
Africa

24 *Opuntia rafinesquii*
North America

25 *Phacelia grandiflora*
North America

26 *Spiraea douglasii*
North America

27 *Dipladenia flava*
USA, Caribbean &
Honduras

28 *Clintonia andrewsiana*
North America

29 *Yucca canaliculata*
USA & Mexico

30 *Iresine herbstii*
North America

31 *Ceanothus lobbianus*
North America

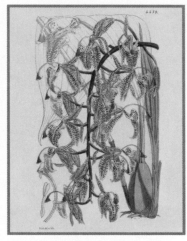

32 *Cycnoches barbatum*
Central & South
America

33 *Dipladenia acuminata*
USA, Central America,
West Indies & South
America

34 *Berberis darwinii*
Argentina & Chile

35 *Pleroma macranthum*
Brazil

36 *Penstemon wrightii*
Mexico & USA

37 *Bougainvillea spectabilis* South America

38 *Philodendron erubescens* Colombia

39 *Ada aurantiaca* Nicaragua & South America

40 *Odontioda* x *vuylstekeae* South America

41 *Grevillea alpestris* Australia

42 *Alocasia metallica* Australia, Oceania & Malaysia

43 *Acacia drummondii* Australia

44 *Swainsona maccullochiana* Australia

Vincent Brooks,Day & Son Imp

L. Reeve & C⁰ London

L Reeve & Cº London

1.

2.

3.

W. Fitch del. et lith.

Vincent Brooks Imp.

W.Fitch del et lith.

Vincent Brooks Imp.

5

M.S.del. J.N.Fitch lith.

Vincent Brooks, Day & Son Lt.dimp.

L. Reeve & C.o London.

M.S.del. J.N.Fitch lith.

Vincent Brooks, Day & Son Ltᵈ imp.

M.S.del. J.N.Fitch lith.

Vincent Brooks,Day & Son Lt⁰ imp

L. Reeve & C⁰ London.

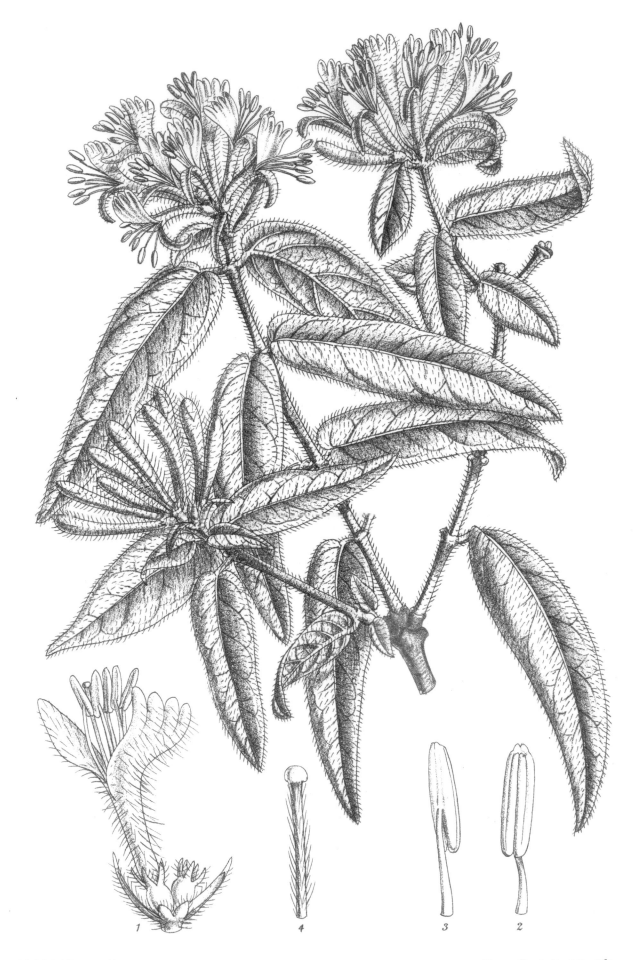

M.S.del J.N.Fitch lith.

Vincent Brooks,Day & Son Lt.ᵈ imp

L. Reeve & Cᵒ London.

Vincent Brooks Day & Son Lt^d imp

L.Reeve & C°London

M.S.del J.N.Fitch.lith.

Vincent Brooks Day & Son Lt‐Imp

4427.

Fitch, del et lith.

R.B.&R.imp.

4680.

Fitch, del et lith.

F. Reeve, imp.

5010.

W. Fitch del.et lith.

Vincent Brooks Imp.

6843.

M.S. del. J.N.Fitch lith.

Vincent Brooks Day & Son Imp

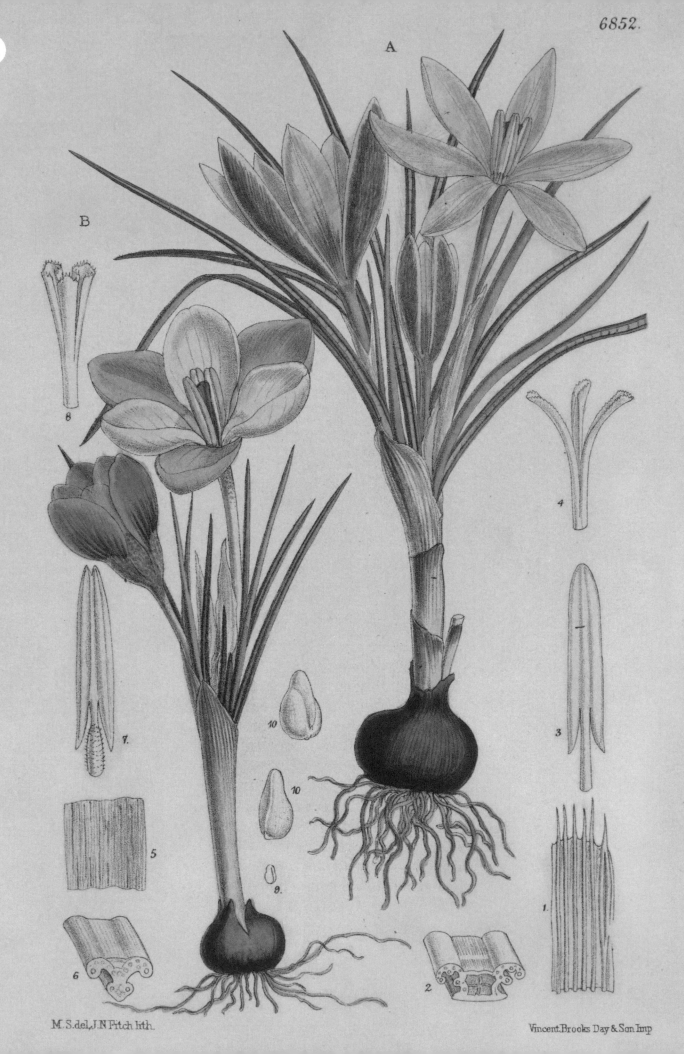

M.S.del.J.N.Fitch lith.

Vincent.Brooks Day & Son.Imp

6852.

A

B

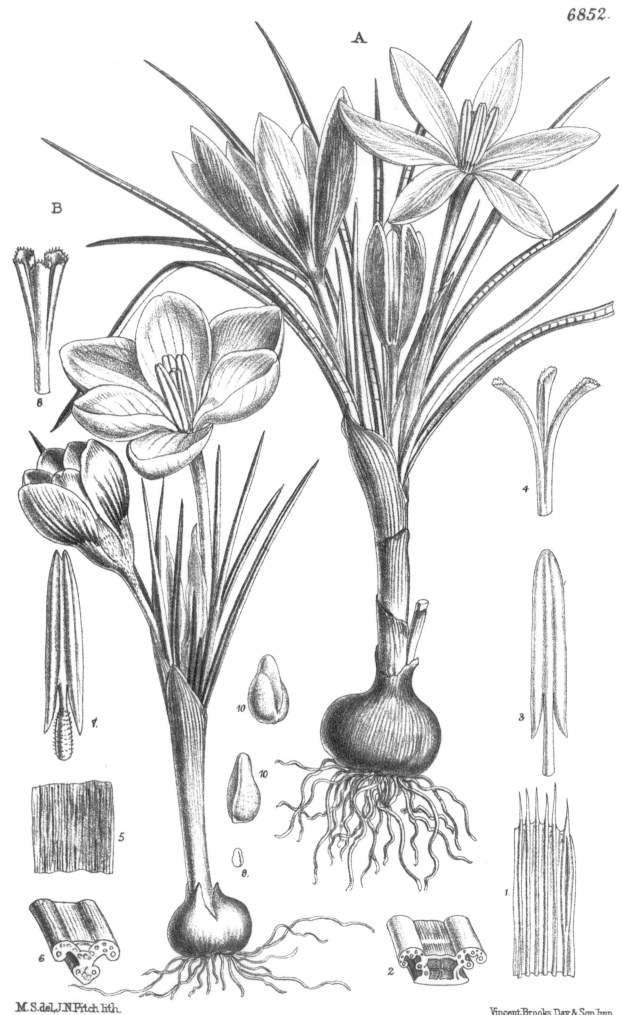

M.S.del, J.N.Fitch lith.

Vincent Brooks Day & Son Imp.

M.S.del. J.N.Fitch lith.

Vincent Brooks Day & Son Ltᵈimp

L.Reeve & Cᵒ London.

5621.

W. Fitch, del. et lith.

Vincent Brooks, Imp.

Vincent Brooks, Imp.

5926.

W. Fitch, del. et lith.

Vincent Brooks, Day & Son, Imp.

W. Fitch, del. et lith.

Vincent Brooks, Day & Son, Imp.

W. Fitch, del. et lith.

Vincent Brooks, Day & Son, Imp.

W. Fitch, del. et lith.

Vincent Brooks, Day & Son, Imp.

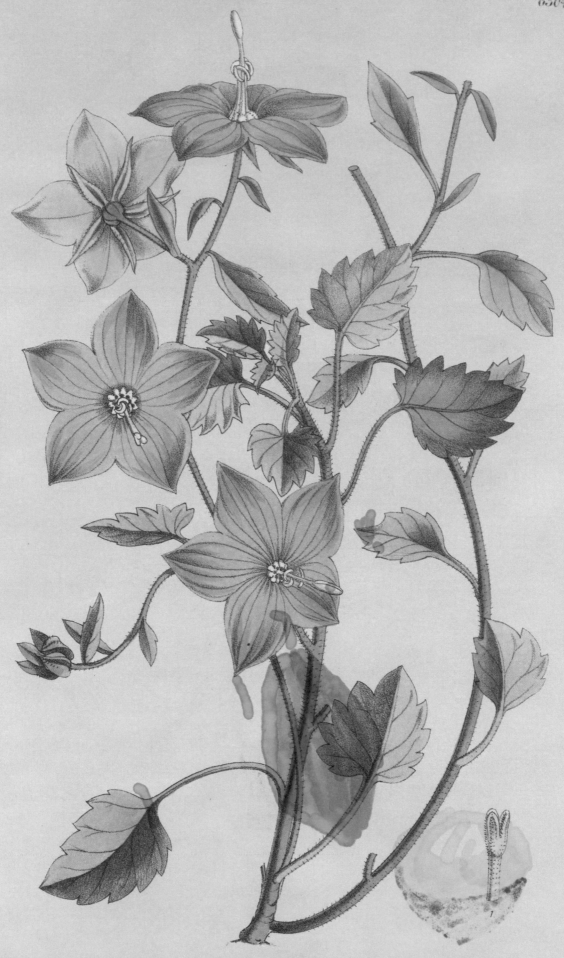

A.B.del J.N.Fitch Lith

Vincent Brooks Day & Son Imp

M.S del. J.N.Fitch lith.

Vincent Brooks Day & Son Imp

L.Reeve & Co London.

M.S.del, J.N.Fitch lith.   Vincent Brooks Day & Son Imp.

L. Reeve & C°. London.

Reeve & Nichols, imp.

Fitch, del et lith.

W. Fitch del. et lith.

Vincent Brooks Imp.

W. Fitch, del. et lith.

Vincent Brooks, Imp.

W.Fitch, del et lith.

Vincent. Brooks Day & Son Imp.

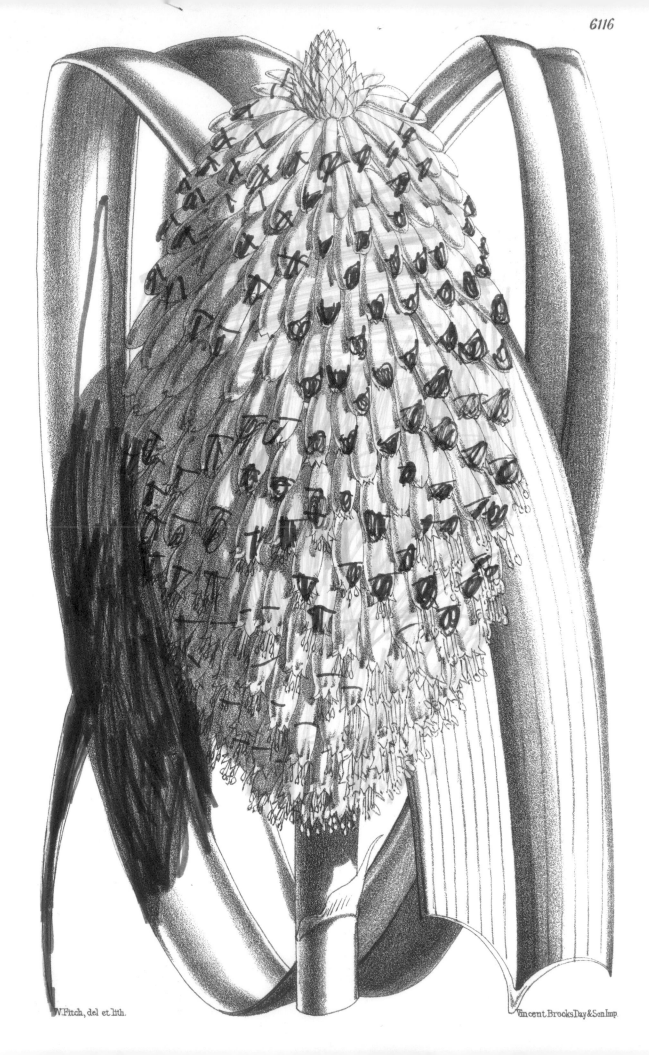

W.Fitch, del et lith.

Vincent Brooks Day & Son Imp.

5378.

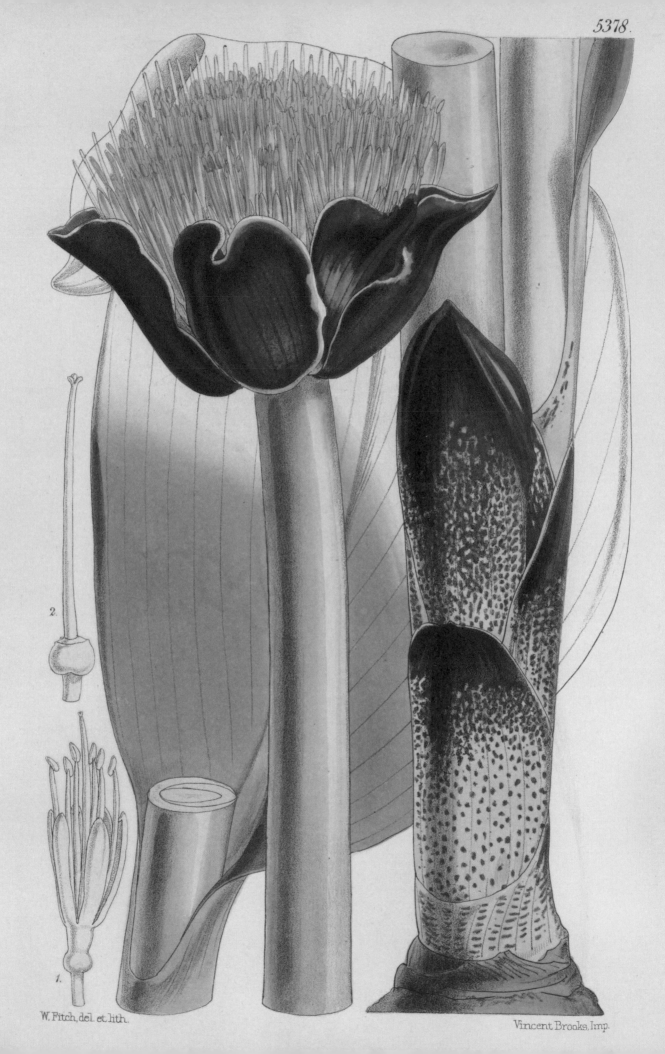

W. Fitch, del. et lith.

Vincent Brooks, Imp.

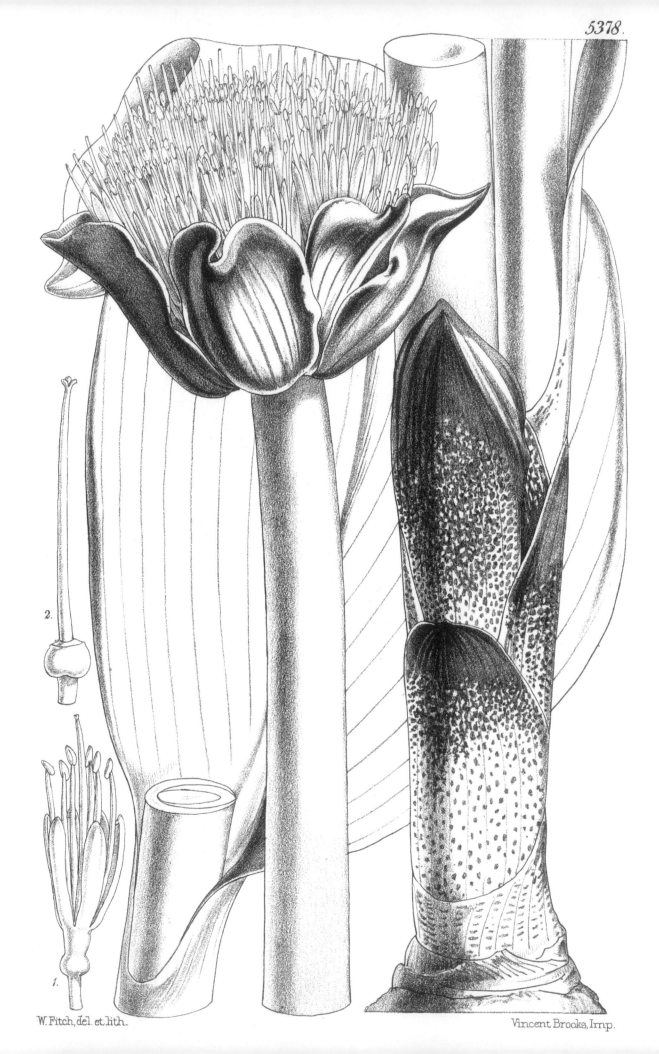

2.

1.

W. Fitch, del. et lith.

Vincent Brooks, Imp.

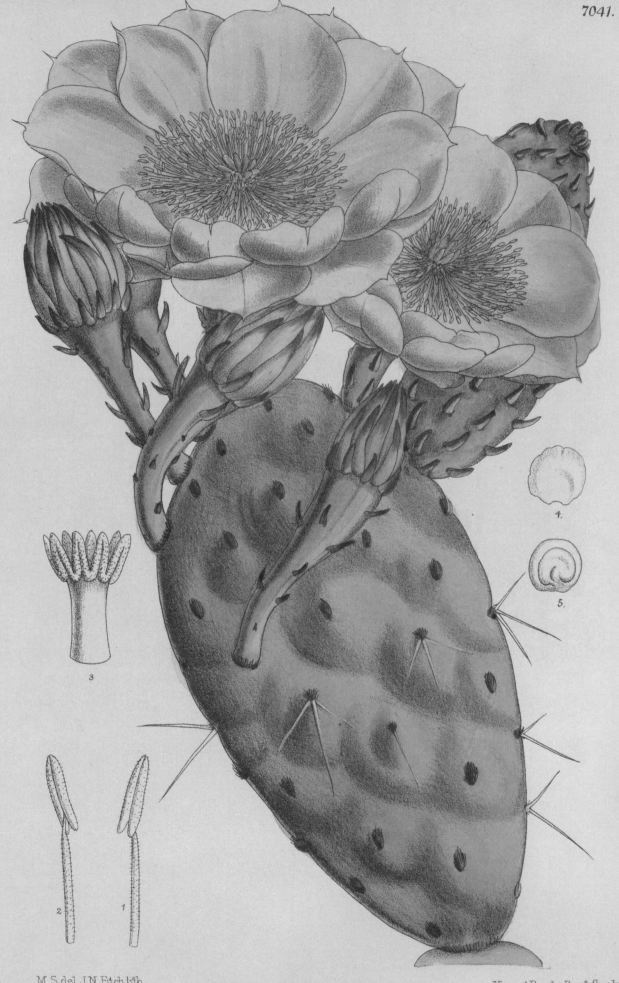

M.S.del, J.N.Fitch lith.

Vincent Brooks Day & Son Imp.

L.Reeve & C.º London.

M.S.del, J.N.Fitch lith.

Vincent Brooks Day & Son Imp.

L Reeve & C? London.

W. Fitch del. et lith.

Vincent Brooks Imp.

W. Fitch del. et lith.

Vincent Brooks Imp

2.

1.

3.

W.Fitch, del.et lith.

Vincent Brooks, Imp.

4702.

Fitch, del et lith.

F. Reeve, imp.

4702.

M.S.del, J.N.Fitch lith.

Vincent Brooks,Day&Son Imp

L. Reeve & C.º London.

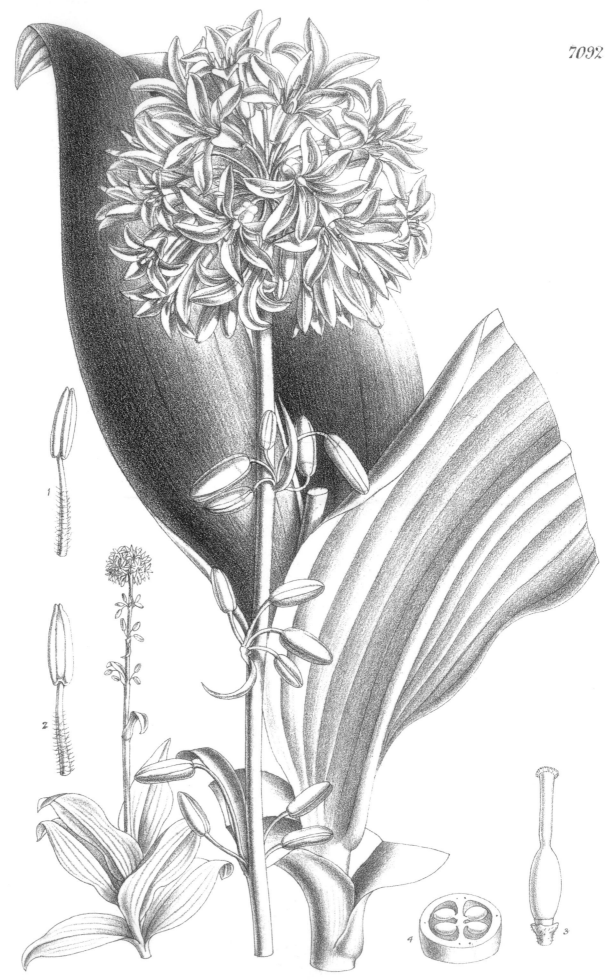

M.S. del, J.N.Fitch lith.

Vincent Brooks,Day & Son Imp.

L Reeve & C⁰ London.

W. Fitch, del. et lith.

2.

Vincent Brooks, Imp.

W. Fitch, del. et lith.

Vincent Brooks, Imp.

1.

2.

W. Fitch, del. et lith.

Vincent Brooks, Imp.

2.

W.Fitch, del.et lith.

Vincent Brooks, Imp.

4811

Fitch del. et lith.

Fitch del. et lith.

Vincent Brooks Imp.

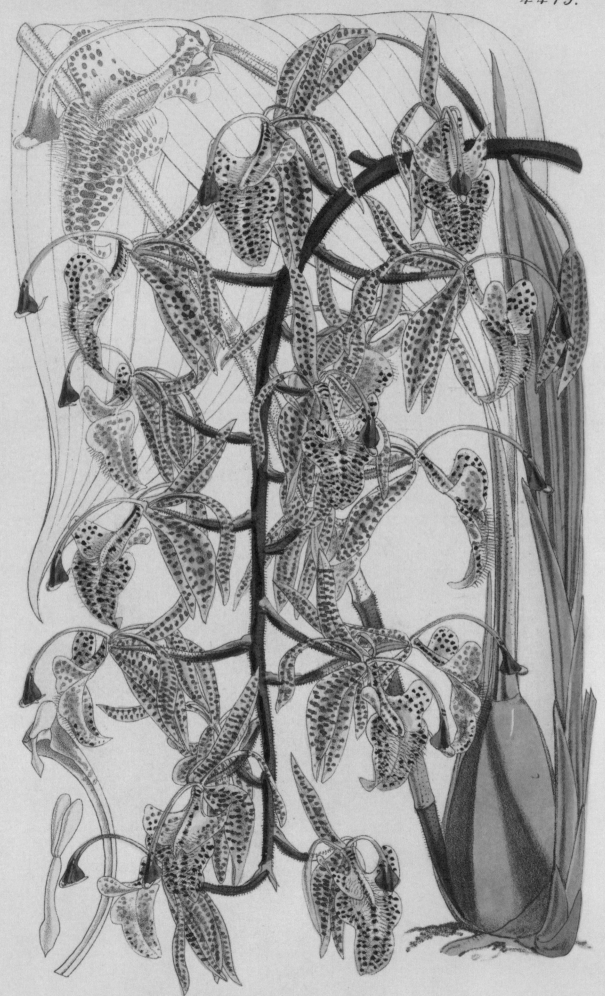

Fitch del et lith.

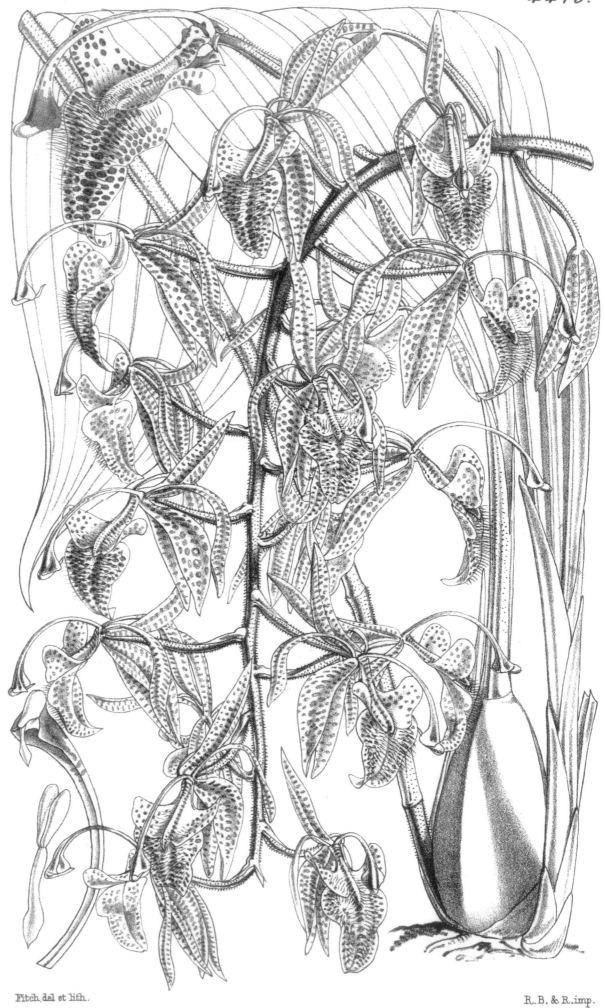

4828

W Fitch del. et lith.

Vincent Brooks Imp.

4828

4590

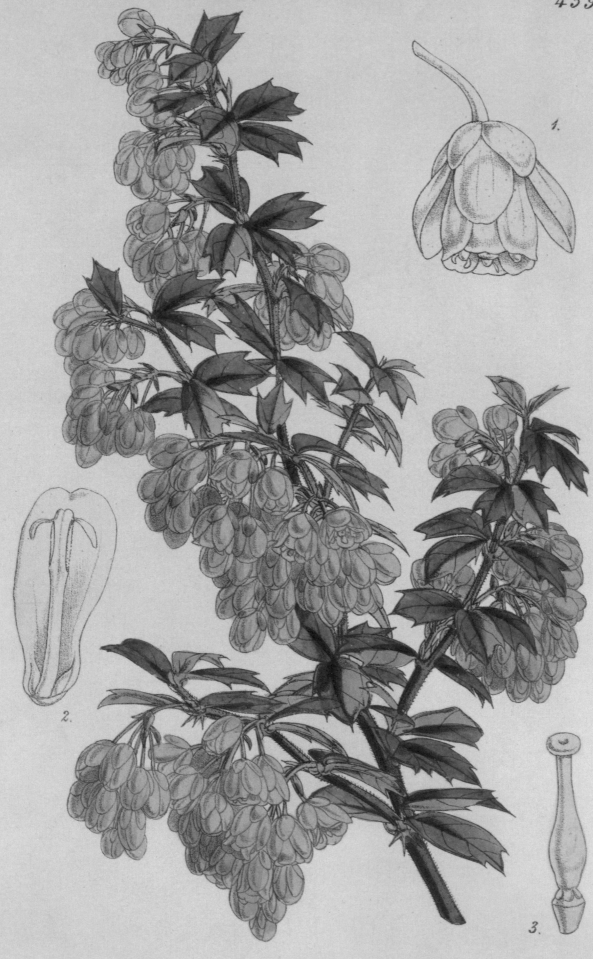

1.

2.

3.

Fitch del et lith.

Reeve & Nichols, imp.

W. Fitch, del. et lith.

Vincent Brooks, Day & Son, Imp.

W. Fitch, del. et lith.

Vincent Brooks, Day & Son, Imp.

1.

Fitch, del. et lith.

Reeve & Nichols, imp.

Fitch, del et. lith.

Reeve & Nichols, imp.

Fitch del. et lith.

Vincent Brooks Imp.

Fitch del. et lith.

Vincent Brooks Imp.

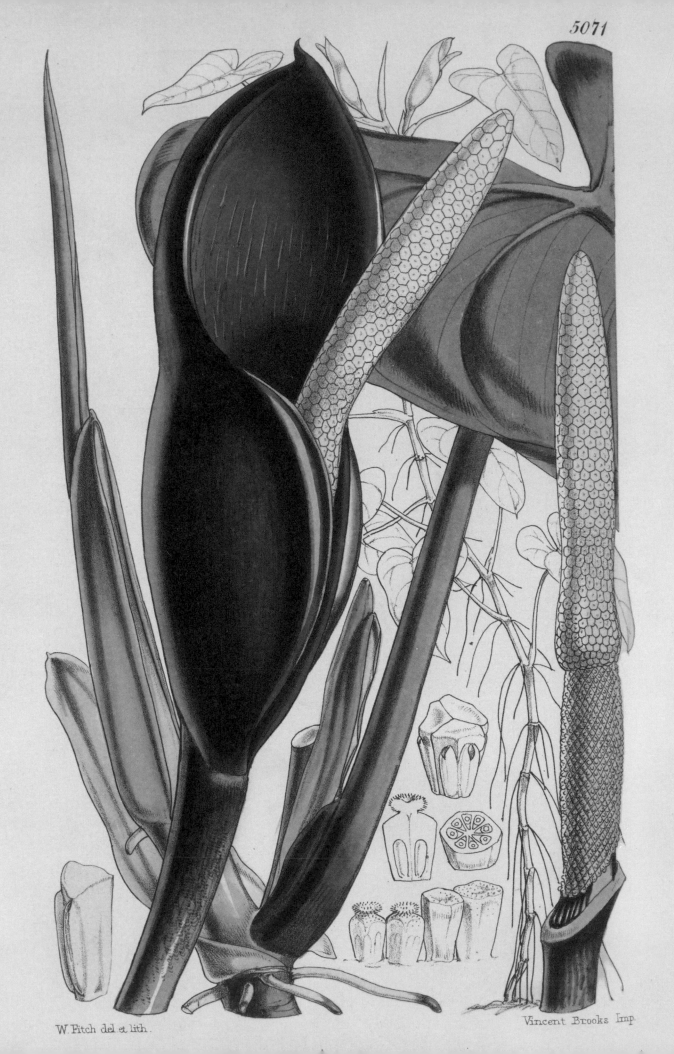

W. Fitch del et lith.

Vincent Brooks Imp.

M.S.del,J.N.Fitch lith.

Vincent Brooks Day & Son Ltᵈ Imp

W. Fitch del. et lith.

Vincent Brooks Imp.

5190.

Vincent Brooks, Imp.

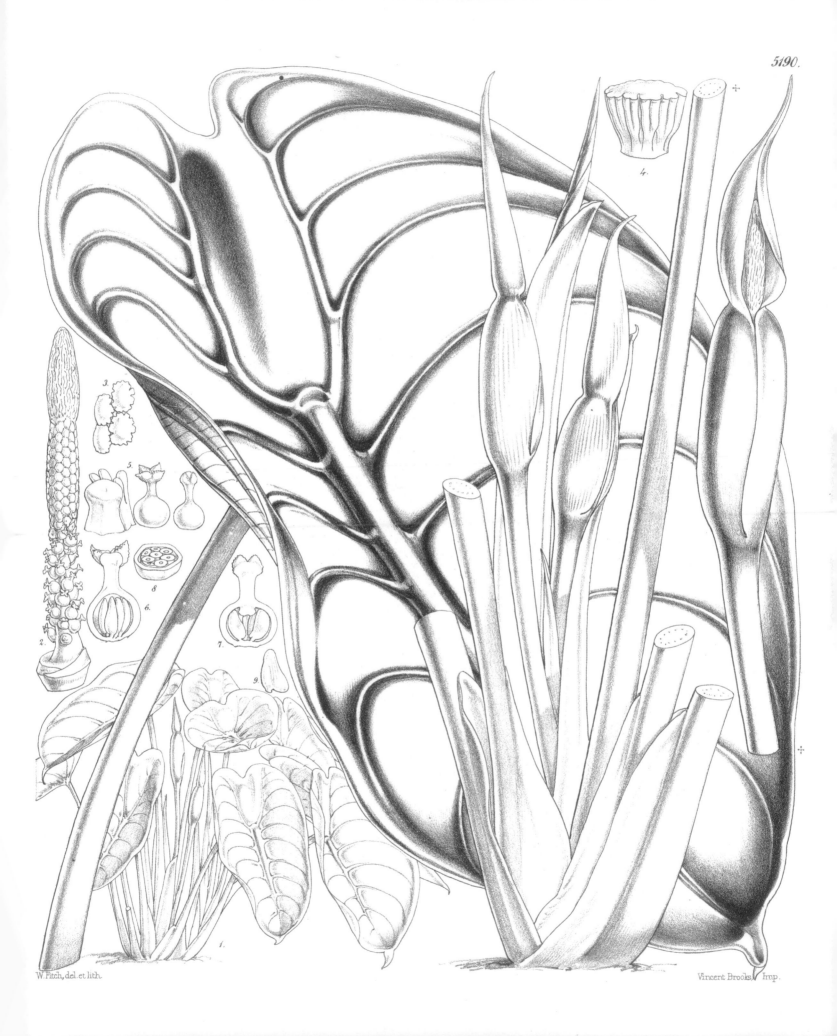

5190.

W. Fitch, del. et lith.

Vincent Brooks, Imp.

1.

2.

W. Fitch, del. et lith.

Vincent Brooks, Imp.

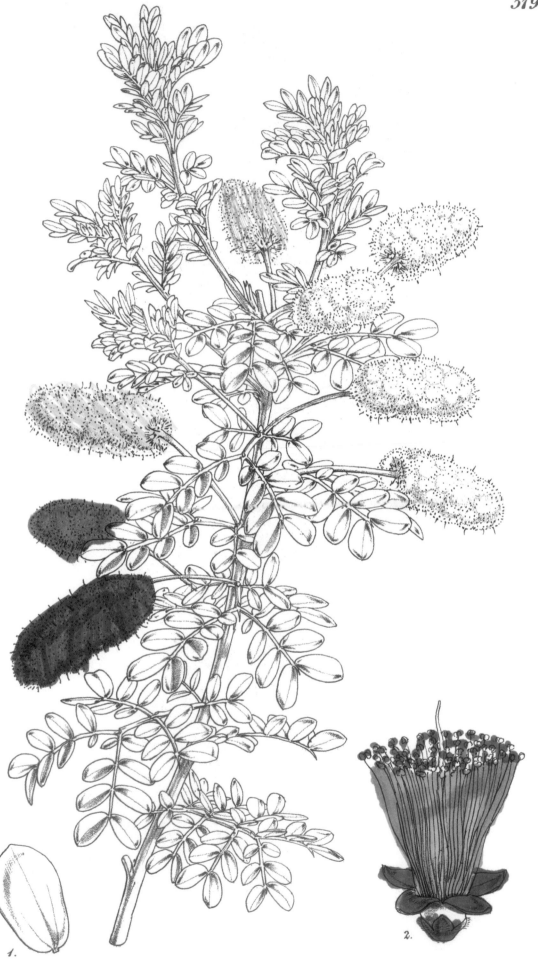

1.

2.

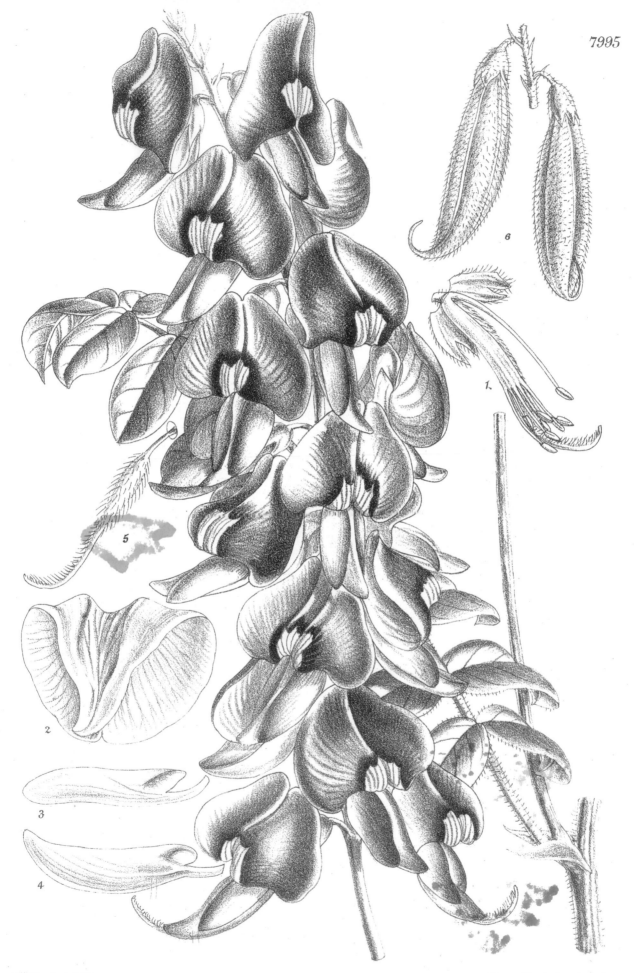